CHEMO DIET (

NEWLY DIAGNOSED

"Nutritious Chemo Diet for newly Diagnosed"

ALLIE NAGEL

Copyright © 2023 by Allie Nagel

DISCLAIMER

This cookbook is intended to provide general information and recipes.

The recipes provided in this cookbook are not intended to replace or be a substitute for medical advice from a physician.

The reader should consult a healthcare professional for any specific medical advice, diagnosis or treatment.

Any specific dietary advice provided in this cookbook is not intended to replace or be a substitute for medical advice from a physician.

The author is not responsible or liable for any adverse effects experienced by readers of this cookbook as a result of following the recipes or dietary advice provided.

The author makes no representations or warranties of any kind (express or implied) as to the accuracy, completeness, reliability or suitability of the recipes provided in this cookbook.

The author disclaims any and all liability for any damages arising out of the use or misuse of the recipes provided in this cookbook. The reader must also take care to ensure that the recipes provided in this cookbook are prepared and cooked safely.

The recipes provided in this cookbook are for informational purposes only and should not be used as a substitute for professional medical advice, diagnosis or treatment.

TABLE OF CONTENTS

INTRODUCTION

One common and essential treatment in the fight against cancer is chemotherapy. It is a vital component of cancer treatment.

It describes the use of medications intended to either kill or stop the spread of cancer cells that divide quickly.

Chemotherapy aims to eradicate malignant cells from the body, focusing on the main tumor as well as any possible metastases.

The medications for chemotherapy function by interfering with the cell cycle, which stops cancer cells from reproducing and dividing.

Regrettably, these medications can also impact the body's healthy, quickly proliferating cells, which can result in adverse consequences like weariness, nausea, hair loss, and an increased risk of infection.

The particular medications taken, the dosage, and the reaction of each patient all affect how severe and what kind of side effects develop.

Your general health and the type and stage of the cancer will determine the medications and treatment strategy that are chosen.

More so, a chemo diet is a specialized eating plan designed to support you undergoing chemotherapy.

A carefully curated chemo diet aims to address the challenges the procedure brings and provide essential nutrients to promote adequate and fast healing and strength during treatment.

Some of the key things to consider during chemotherapy include: Adequate Protein Intake, hydration, nutrient-rich foods, small, frequent Meals, anti-inflammatory foods, avoiding certain foods that interact negatively with chemotherapy drugs or exacerbate side effects like spicy foods, citrus fruits, or high-fiber items, supplements

Finally, a chemo diet is not one-size-fits-all, your needs may vary from another person's which is why I strongly advice that you consult with a registered dietitian or healthcare practitioner to help out with your personal preferences and dietary requirements.

CHAPTER 1

15 COMMON SIDE EFFECTS AND CHALLENGES DURING CHEMOTHERAPY

1. Chemotherapy has the potential to induce nausea and vomiting by activating the brain's vomiting area.
2. Throughout treatment, you may continue to feel extremely exhausted and lacking in energy.
3. Chemotherapy affects hair follicles by targeting quickly dividing cells, which results in hair loss.
4. Weakness and exhaustion can be caused by anemia, which is a low red blood cell count.
5. Chemotherapy weakens the immune system, which makes a patient more vulnerable to infections.
6. Injury to the mouth's quickly proliferating cells can result in excruciating sores and make swallowing difficult.
7. Chemotherapy may cause taste buds to shift, which could result in altered appetite and weight loss.

8. When nerves are damaged, it can cause pain, tingling, or numbness, particularly in the hands and feet.

9. During chemotherapy, the skin may become dry, sensitive, or discolored.

10. Chemotherapy medications may have an impact on the digestive system, resulting in abnormalities of the colon.

11. Memory, focus, and cognitive function are issues that some patients face.

12. Chemotherapy may affect the reproductive cells, resulting in either irreversible or transient infertility.

13. Lower platelet levels might make bruising easier and bleeding more likely.

14. Edema, or swelling and retention of fluid, can happen, particularly in the extremities.

15. Coping with the physical side effects of chemotherapy can lead to emotional discomfort, despair, and anxiety.

FOODS TO EAT AND AVOID DURING CHEMO

FOODS TO EAT

1. Boost the immune system and help repair tissue. Lean meats, poultry, fish, eggs, and dairy products are a few examples.

2. Supply vital minerals, vitamins, and antioxidants. To ensure a well-balanced nutrient intake, select a variety.

3. Provide a healthy amount of fiber and energy. Incorporate whole grains such as whole wheat, quinoa, and brown rice.

4. To promote general health, include foods high in healthy fats, such as avocados, nuts, seeds, and olive oil.

5. Eat foods high in water content, such as oranges, cucumbers, and melons, to stay hydrated, particularly if you're feeling queasy.

6. Known for its anti-nausea qualities, ginger can help with nausea brought on by chemotherapy.

7. Include fermented foods with good bacteria, such as yogurt and kefir, to support gut health.

8. For an excellent supply of protein and calcium without too much saturated fat, aim for low-fat dairy products.

9. Eating more frequently and in smaller portions will help control hunger and avoid nausea.

10. They can be easy to digest and offer hydration, so they're a good option when you're not feeling too hungry.

FOODS TO AVOID

1. Avoid consuming too many foods that have artificial ingredients, preservatives, and additives.

2. Consuming too much sugar can cause energy surges and crashes. Use natural sweeteners sparingly.

3. Foods high in fat might be difficult to digest and may cause nausea. Select healthier cooking techniques.

4. During chemotherapy, some people may become sensitive to caffeine. Observe how it affects you and make the necessary adjustments.

5. Foods that are spicy might aggravate symptoms like nausea and mouth sores by irritating the digestive tract.

6. Alcohol may cause dehydration and have unfavorable interactions with several chemotherapy medications.

7. Steer clear of raw or undercooked meats, eggs, and shellfish to lower your chance of contracting a foodborne illness.

8. If you have stomach pain or mouth sores, try limiting your intake of acidic foods like citrus fruits.

9. Although fiber is necessary, too much of it can be difficult to digest. Choose a moderate amount of fiber.

10. To aid in digestion and control any potential nausea, concentrate on smaller, nutrient-dense meals instead.

NUTRITION BASICS FOR CHEMO PATIENTS

15 Nutritional requirements during chemotherapy.

1. Make sure you consume enough calories to keep your energy up and meet your body's needs while undergoing chemotherapy.

2. For tissue repair and immunological support, include sources of high-quality protein such as lean meats, poultry, fish, eggs, lentils, and dairy.

3. Maintain adequate hydration to prevent chemotherapy-induced dehydration and to promote general health.

4. Eat a range of fruits and vegetables to acquire the vitamins and minerals your body needs for healthy immune system operation and general wellbeing.

5. To prevent or treat anemia, eat foods high in iron, such as lean meats, beans, lentils, and fortified cereals.

6. For the health of your bones, make sure you're getting enough calcium and vitamin D. Good sources

include dairy products, fortified plant-based substitutes, and sunlight.

7. To promote digestive health, include fiber from fruits, vegetables, and whole grains. Adapt your intake of fiber to your tolerance.

8. For energy and general well-being, include sources of healthy fats such avocados, nuts, seeds, and olive oil.

9. To help combat oxidative stress, eat foods high in antioxidants, such as berries, leafy greens, and bright vegetables.

10. To improve energy metabolism, make sure you are getting enough B vitamins from foods like whole grains, leafy greens, and lean proteins.

11. Rich sources of anti-inflammatory omega-3 fatty acids include walnuts, flaxseeds, chia seeds, and fatty fish.

12. To provide you long-lasting energy, choose complex carbohydrates found in whole grains, legumes, and vegetables.

13. Eat foods high in probiotics, such as kefir and yogurt, to improve gut health, particularly if you're experiencing digestive problems.

14. Consult a qualified dietitian to develop a nutrition plan that takes into account each person's preferences, challenges, and tolerances.

15. Speak with medical experts to find out if you need to take certain dietary supplements to treat nutrient shortages or chemotherapy side effects.

15 Importance of staying hydrated.

1. Water is vital for healthy cellular function because it facilitates the metabolic activities that are needed to life.

2. Sweating and heat dissipation are two ways that enough water helps control body temperature.

3. Water is an essential component for the bloodstream's ability to carry nutrients to all of the body's cells.

4. Drinking enough water keeps joints cushioned and lubricated, which promotes fluid motion.

5. Water promotes healthy digestion, helps nutrients dissolve and move through the body, and keeps constipation at bay.

6. Staying properly hydrated helps the kidneys filter out waste and help the body get rid of it.

7. Better concentration, mental alertness, and enhanced cognitive function are associated with drinking enough water.

8. Maintaining blood volume through proper hydration supports circulation and heart function.

9. Hydration supports a healthy complexion by enhancing the flexibility and hydration of the skin.

10. The body needs water to keep electrolytes like sodium and potassium in balance.

11. Staying hydrated is essential for achieving peak physical performance as it helps avoid weariness and cramping that come with dehydration.

12. It is crucial to maintain adequate fluids since dehydration can trigger both headaches and migraines.

13. Consuming water prior to meals may increase feelings of fullness and help with weight management.

14. Hydration aids in the movement of antibodies and immunological cells, which strengthens the immune system.

15. The importance of water for emotional health is highlighted by the fact that dehydration can have a detrimental effect on mood and exacerbate feelings of weariness and irritability.

15 Tips and Tricks on how to maintain a healthy weight

1. A balanced diet should consist of a range of foods high in nutrients, such as fruits, vegetables, whole grains, lean meats, and healthy fats.

2. To prevent overindulging and preserve the proper ratio of calories, pay attention to portion sizes.

3. To enhance general fitness and weight control, engage in regular exercise that combines both aerobic and strength training activities.

4. To promote metabolism and aid with hunger management, consume a sufficient amount of water each day.

5. To avoid emotional or overeating, pay attention to your body's signals of hunger and fullness.

6. Choose entire, unprocessed foods instead of processed, sugar-filled ones.

7. Select meals high in fiber, such as fruits, vegetables, and whole grains, to help your digestive system and encourage feelings of fullness.

8. To help maintain muscle mass and satiety, include lean protein sources including fish, chicken, beans, and tofu.

9. To keep blood sugar levels constant and prevent acute hunger, eat regular, balanced meals and snacks.

10. Sufficient and high-quality sleep should be prioritized because insufficient sleep can upset hormone balance and lead to weight gain.

11. Put stress-reduction techniques into practice because long-term stress can cause emotional eating and weight increase.

12. To stay motivated and focused, set realistic and attainable goals for managing your weight.

13. To promote awareness and accountability, measure your food consumption and physical activity using an app or by keeping a food journal.

14. To keep an eye on your general health and take care of any underlying problems that could affect your weight, schedule routine checkups.

15. Seek advice and help on weight control from healthcare professionals, such as nutritionists or registered dietitians, for individualized recommendations.

15 Tips and Tricks on how to Balance macronutrients

1. **Carbohydrates:** Give the body energy. For long-lasting energy, go for complex carbs found in whole grains, legumes, and veggies.

2. **Proteins:** Required for immunological response and tissue healing. Add fish, poultry, eggs, dairy, legumes, and plant-based proteins to your diet, along with lean meats.

3. **Fats:** Required for the synthesis of hormones and the uptake of nutrients. Add in your share of heart-healthy fats from nuts, seeds, avocados, and olive oil.

4. **Fiber:** A component of carbs, fiber aids in maintaining stable blood sugar levels and promotes digestive health. Add healthful grains, fruits, and veggies.

5. **Hydration:** Although it's not a macronutrient, maintaining adequate hydration is essential for good health. Water helps in temperature regulation, nutrition transfer, and digestion.

6. **Balanced Meals:** To provide a wide range of nutrients and long-lasting energy, aim for meals that include a mix of carbohydrates, proteins, and fats.

7. **Portion Control:** Regulate portion sizes to prevent overindulgence and preserve a balanced, healthful intake of macronutrients.

8. **Meal Timing:** To ensure a consistent source of energy, distribute macronutrients throughout the day with frequent meals and snacks.

9. **Nutrient Timing (for Exercise):** For best results and recuperation, plan your nutrition around exercise,

consuming a combination of proteins and carbs both before and after a workout.

10. **Customized Needs:** Modify macronutrient ratios in accordance with each person's metabolic requirements, activity level, and health objectives.

11. **Quality of Macronutrients:** To guarantee a high-quality intake of vital nutrients, pick sources of proteins, lipids, and carbs that are high in nutrients.

12. **Mindful Eating:** To preserve a positive relationship with food, engage in mindful eating by being aware of your hunger and fullness signs.

13. **Dietary Variety:** To guarantee a wide range of nutrients and avoid nutrient deficits, eat a variety of meals.

14. **Cooking Techniques:** To retain the nutritional content of food, use healthy cooking techniques like baking, grilling, or steaming.

15. **Speak with a Nutritionist:** Create a customized macronutrient balance with the help of a certified dietitian to meet your unique health needs and objectives.

14 Key vitamins and minerals for chemo patients.

1. **Vitamin D:** Vital for strong bones. Dietary sources such as fatty fish and fortified foods, as well as sun exposure, might also be factors.

2. **Calcium:** necessary for strong bones. Add fortified plant-based substitutes or dairy products to the diet.

3. **Iron:** Essential for controlling or avoiding anemia. Good sources include lean meats, beans, lentils, and fortified cereals.

4. **Folate:** Facilitates the production and repair of DNA. Leafy greens, legumes, and fortified cereals contain it.

5. **Vitamin B12:** Essential for healthy nerve cells. Add foods enriched with nutrients or animal products as sources.

6. **Vitamin C:** Strengthens the immune system and facilitates the absorption of iron. Vegetables, berries, and citrus fruits are excellent sources.

7. **Zinc:** Boosts the immune system. Incorporate sources such as dairy, meat, nuts, and legumes.

8. **Magnesium:** Essential for nerve and muscle function. Good sources include leafy greens, whole grains, nuts, and seeds.

9. **Potassium:** Promotes healthy muscle and cardiac function. Foods high in potassium include oranges, tomatoes, potatoes, and bananas.

10. **Vitamin A:** Essential for healthy immune system and vision. Add leafy greens, sweet potatoes, and carrots.

11. **Vitamin K:** Vitamin K is necessary for the coagulation of blood. Broccoli, Brussels sprouts, and leafy greens are excellent sources.

12. **Phosphorus:** Vital to the health of bones. present in meat, dairy, and whole grains.

13. **Selenium:** Has anti-oxidant properties. Add sources such as poultry, seafood, and Brazil nuts.

14. **Choline:** Essential for the health of the liver. Broccoli, beef, and eggs are healthy food choices.

30 significances of fiber and antioxidants.

Fiber Significance:

1. **Digestive Health:** Fiber helps maintain a healthy digestive tract by encouraging regular bowel movements, which wards off constipation.

2. **Weight control:** Eating meals high in fiber helps regulate hunger and promotes a feeling of fullness.

3. **Blood Sugar Control:** Soluble fiber is good for those with diabetes because it slows down the absorption of sugar, which helps control blood sugar levels.

4. **Heart Health:** By lowering cholesterol, soluble fiber lowers the risk of heart disease.

5. **Preventing Colorectal Cancer:** Consuming enough fiber is linked to a decreased chance of developing colorectal cancer.

6. **Support for the Gut Microbiota:** Fiber functions as a prebiotic, encouraging the development of advantageous gut bacteria and bolstering the microbiome.

7. **Stabilizing Blood Pressure:** Diets high in dietary fiber may help to reduce blood pressure, according to certain research.

8. **Weight Loss Aid:** Foods high in fiber frequently contain less calories, making them a good choice for people trying to reduce weight.

9. **Decreased Risk of Diverticular Disease:** Consuming enough fiber is linked to a decreased risk of the colon disease diverticular disease.

10. **Enhanced Insulin Sensitivity:** Fiber has the potential to enhance insulin sensitivity, which could aid in the management of illnesses such as metabolic syndrome.

11. **Reduced Overeating and Satiety:** Eating meals high in fiber makes you feel fuller and less likely to overeat.

12. **Improved Nutrient Absorption:** Soluble fiber has the ability to assist slow down the digestive process and increase absorption of nutrients, resulting in improved absorption in the anus.

13. **Steady Energy Release:** Diets rich in fiber help to provide maintained energy levels by facilitating a slower energy release.

14. **Maintenance of a Healthy Weight:** By encouraging a healthy metabolism, a diet high in fiber may help maintain a healthy weight.

15. **Disease Prevention:** Consuming enough fiber has been associated with a lower chance of developing a number of chronic conditions, such as type 2 diabetes and cardiovascular disease.

Antioxidants' Significance

16. Antioxidants have the ability to neutralize free radicals, thereby shielding cells from the damaging effects of oxidative stress.

17. **Support for the immunological System:** Antioxidants assist the body fight off infections and illnesses by bolstering the immunological system.

18. **Heart Health:** By halting oxidative damage to blood vessels and arteries, antioxidants may help lower the risk of heart disease.

19. **Cancer Prevention:** By preventing the formation of aberrant cells, some antioxidants are linked to a

decreased chance of developing specific types of cancer.

20. **Skin Health:** By shielding the skin from UV radiation and other environmental contaminants, antioxidants such as vitamins C and E help maintain healthy skin.

21. **Protection of Vision:** Antioxidants that lower the risk of age-related macular degeneration, such as lutein and zeaxanthin, are good for the health of the eyes.

22. **Anti-Inflammatory Effects:** Due to their anti-inflammatory qualities, antioxidants can help reduce chronic inflammation, which is connected to a number of disorders.

23. **Neurological Health:** By shielding neurons from oxidative stress and possibly lowering the risk of neurodegenerative disorders, antioxidants promote brain health.

24. **Blood Sugar Regulation:** Antioxidants with certain properties may be able to assist in controlling blood sugar levels, which may be advantageous for diabetics.

25. **Joint Health:** Antioxidants have the ability to improve illnesses like arthritis by reducing joint inflammation.

26. **Reproductive Health:** By shielding sperm and eggs from oxidative damage, antioxidants help to sustain reproductive health.

27. **Decreased Oxidative Stress from Exercise:** Consuming antioxidants on a regular basis will help lessen the oxidative stress brought on by vigorous exercise.

28. **Support for Detoxification:** Certain antioxidants contribute to the body's natural processes of detoxification, helping the body get rid of toxic chemicals.

29. **Longevity:** By lowering the body's overall oxidative damage, antioxidants are associated with a possible increase in longevity.

30. **Cognitive Function:** By shielding brain cells from oxidative damage, antioxidants may help memory and cognitive function.

CHAPTER 3

14-DAY MEAL PLAN

DAY 1

Breakfast: Soft Baked Apples with Cinnamon

Lunch: Tofu Stir-Fry

Dinner: Salmon and Avocado Sushi Bowls

DAY 2

Breakfast: Greek Yogurt Parfait

Lunch: Quinoa Salad with Vegetables

Dinner: Roasted Vegetable Quiche

DAY 3

Breakfast: Quinoa Porridge

Lunch: Baked Cod with Herbs

Dinner: Creamy Butternut Squash Soup

DAY 4

Breakfast: Mashed Avocado Toast

Lunch: Mashed Sweet Potatoes

Dinner: Chickpea and Spinach Curry

DAY 5

Breakfast: Coconut Rice Pudding

Lunch: Baked Chicken Breast with Roasted Vegetables

Dinner: Baked Turkey Meatballs with Zucchini Noodles

DAY 6

Breakfast: Avocado and Mango Smoothie

Lunch: Avocado and Chickpea Salad

Dinner: Mashed Sweet Potatoes with Grilled Chicken

DAY 7

Breakfast: Peanut Butter and Banana Smoothie

Lunch: Egg Salad Lettuce Wraps

Dinner: Baked Chicken with Sweet Potatoes and Green Beans

DAY 8

Breakfast: Chia Seed Pudding

Lunch: Salmon and Avocado Wrap

Dinner: Ginger Turmeric Chicken Soup

DAY 9

Breakfast: Scrambled Eggs with Spinach

Lunch: Chicken and Rice Soup

Dinner: Cauliflower and Broccoli Gratin

DAY 10

Breakfast: Banana Pancakes

Lunch: Ginger Carrot Soup

Dinner: Lentil and Vegetable Stew

DAY 11

Breakfast: Soft Baked Apples with Cinnamon

Lunch: Tofu Stir-Fry

Dinner: Salmon and Avocado Sushi Bowls

DAY 12

Breakfast: Greek Yogurt Parfait

Lunch: Quinoa Salad with Vegetables

Dinner: Roasted Vegetable Quiche

DAY 13

Breakfast: Quinoa Porridge

Lunch: Baked Cod with Herbs

Dinner: Creamy Butternut Squash Soup

DAY 14

Breakfast: Mashed Avocado Toast

Lunch: Mashed Sweet Potatoes

Dinner: Chickpea and Spinach Curry

CHAPTER 3

30 NUTRITIOUS RECIPES FOR A CHEMO DIET FOR NEWLY DIAGNOSED

BREAKFAST

Soft Baked Apples with Cinnamon

Preparation Time: 10 minutes

Serves: 4

Calories: 100

Ingredients:

Apples

Cinnamon

Honey (optional)

Method of Preparation:

1. Preheat the oven to 350°F (175°C).
2. Core and slice the apples.

3. Place the apple slices in a baking dish.

4. Sprinkle cinnamon over the apple slices.

5. Optional: Drizzle honey for added sweetness.

6. Bake for 20-25 minutes or until the apples are soft.

Greek Yogurt Parfait

Preparation Time: 5 minutes

Serves: 2

Calories: 200

Ingredients:

Greek yogurt

Fresh berries

Granola

Honey (optional)

Method of Preparation:

1. In a glass or bowl, layer Greek yogurt at the bottom.

2. Add a layer of fresh berries.

3. Sprinkle granola on top.

4. Repeat the layers.

5. Optional: Drizzle honey for sweetness.

Quinoa Porridge

Preparation Time: 15 minutes

Serves: 3

Calories: 250

Ingredients:

Quinoa

Milk (dairy or plant-based)

Maple syrup

Sliced fruits (e.g., banana, berries)

Method of Preparation:

1. Rinse quinoa under cold water.
2. Combine quinoa and milk in a saucepan.
3. Bring to a boil, then reduce heat and simmer until quinoa is cooked.
4. Sweeten with maple syrup.
5. Top with sliced fruits.

Mashed Avocado Toast

Preparation Time: 5 minutes

Serves: 2

Calories: 150

Ingredients:

Whole-grain bread

Avocado

Lemon juice

Salt and pepper

Method of Preparation:

1. Toast the whole-grain bread.
2. Mash the avocado and mix with lemon juice, salt, and pepper.
3. Spread the mashed avocado on the toasted bread.

Coconut Rice Pudding

Preparation Time: 30 minutes

Serves: 4

Calories: 200 **Sodium:**

Ingredients:

White rice

Coconut milk

Sugar or sweetener of choice

Vanilla extract

Cinnamon (optional)

Method of Preparation:

1. Cook the white rice according to package instructions.
2. In a separate saucepan, combine coconut milk, cooked rice, sugar, and vanilla extract.
3. Simmer on low heat until the mixture thickens.
4. Optional: Sprinkle with cinnamon before serving.

Avocado and Mango Smoothie

Preparation Time: 5 minutes

Serves: 2

Calories: 250

Ingredients:

Ripe avocado

Ripe mango

Greek yogurt

Honey or agave syrup

Almond milk

Method of Preparation:

1. Peel and pit the avocado and mango.
2. In a blender, combine avocado, mango, Greek yogurt, honey, and almond milk.
3. Blend until smooth and creamy.

Peanut Butter and Banana Smoothie

Preparation Time: 5 minutes

Serves: 2

Calories: 300

Ingredients:

Banana

Peanut butter

Greek yogurt

Milk (dairy or plant-based)

Ice cubes (optional)

Method of Preparation:

1. Peel the banana.
2. In a blender, combine banana, peanut butter, Greek yogurt, and milk.
3. Add ice cubes if desired.
4. Blend until smooth.

Chia Seed Pudding

Preparation Time: 5 minutes (plus chilling time)

Serves: 2

Calories: 150

Ingredients:

Chia seeds

Milk (dairy or plant-based)

Sweetener of choice (e.g., honey, maple syrup)

Vanilla extract

Fresh fruits (optional)

Method of Preparation:

1. In a bowl, mix chia seeds, milk, sweetener, and vanilla extract.
2. Stir well and let it sit for 5 minutes.
3. Stir again and refrigerate for at least 2 hours or overnight.
4. Before serving, top with fresh fruits if desired.

Scrambled Eggs with Spinach

Preparation Time: 10 minutes

Serves: 2

Calories: 200

Ingredients:

Eggs

Fresh spinach

Salt and pepper

Olive oil or butter

Method of Preparation:

1. In a bowl, beat the eggs and season with salt and pepper.
2. Heat olive oil or butter in a pan over medium heat.
3. Add fresh spinach to the pan and sauté until wilted.
4. Pour beaten eggs over spinach and scramble until cooked through.

Banana Pancakes

Preparation Time: 15 minutes

Serves: 2

Calories: 250

Ingredients:

Ripe bananas

Eggs

Baking powder

Cinnamon (optional)

Maple syrup (optional)

Method of Preparation:

1. In a bowl, mash ripe bananas.
2. Add eggs, baking powder, and cinnamon. Mix until well combined.
3. Heat a non-stick pan and ladle small portions of the batter.
4. Cook until bubbles form, then flip and cook the other side.

LUNCH

Tofu Stir-Fry

Preparation Time: 20 minutes

Serves: 4

Calories: 250

Ingredients:

Firm tofu

Mixed vegetables (broccoli, bell peppers, carrots, etc.)

Soy sauce

Garlic

Ginger

Sesame oil

Olive oil

Brown rice (optional)

Method of Preparation:

1. Press tofu to remove excess water and cut into cubes.
2. Sauté minced garlic and ginger in olive oil.
3. Add tofu cubes and stir until golden.
4. Add mixed vegetables and stir-fry until tender.
5. Pour soy sauce and sesame oil, stir well.
6. Serve over brown rice if desired.

Quinoa Salad with Vegetables

Preparation Time: 25 minutes

Serves: 4

Calories: 200 **Sodium:**

Ingredients:

Quinoa

Mixed vegetables (cucumber, cherry tomatoes, bell peppers, etc.)

Olive oil

Lemon juice

Fresh herbs (e.g., parsley, mint)

Salt and pepper

Method of Preparation:

1. Cook quinoa according to package instructions.
2. Chop mixed vegetables and herbs.
3. In a bowl, combine quinoa, vegetables, olive oil, lemon juice, herbs, salt, and pepper.
4. Toss well and refrigerate before serving.

Baked Cod with Herbs

Preparation Time: 20 minutes

Serves: 4

Calories: 150

Ingredients:

Cod fillets

Olive oil

Lemon juice

Garlic

Fresh herbs (e.g., thyme, rosemary)

Salt and pepper

Method of Preparation:

1. Preheat the oven to 375°F (190°C).
2. Place cod fillets in a baking dish.
3. Drizzle with olive oil and lemon juice.
4. Season with minced garlic, fresh herbs, salt, and pepper.
5. Bake for 15-20 minutes or until fish flakes easily.

Mashed Sweet Potatoes

Preparation Time: 30 minutes

Serves: 4

Calories: 120

Ingredients:

Sweet potatoes

Butter or margarine

Milk (dairy or plant-based)

Salt and nutmeg (optional)

Method of Preparation:

1. Peel and cube sweet potatoes.
2. Boil until tender, then drain.
3. Mash with butter, milk, salt, and nutmeg if desired.

Baked Chicken Breast with Roasted Vegetables

Preparation Time: 30 minutes

Serves: 4

Calories: 250

Ingredients:

Chicken breasts

Assorted vegetables (e.g., carrots, bell peppers, zucchini)

Olive oil

Garlic powder

Paprika

Salt and pepper

Method of Preparation:

1. Preheat the oven to 400°F (200°C).
2. Season chicken breasts with garlic powder, paprika, salt, and pepper.
3. Arrange chicken breasts and chopped vegetables on a baking sheet.
4. Drizzle with olive oil and bake for 20-25 minutes or until chicken is cooked through.

Avocado and Chickpea Salad

Preparation Time: 15 minutes

Serves: 4

Calories: 200 **Sodium:**

Ingredients:

Ripe avocados

Chickpeas (canned, drained)

Cherry tomatoes

Red onion

Cilantro

Lime juice

Olive oil

Salt and pepper

Method of Preparation:

1. Dice avocados, cherry tomatoes, and red onion.
2. In a bowl, combine avocados, chickpeas, tomatoes, red onion, and chopped cilantro.
3. Drizzle with lime juice and olive oil.
4. Season with salt and pepper, toss gently.

Egg Salad Lettuce Wraps

Preparation Time: 15 minutes

Serves: 4

Calories: 150

Ingredients:

Hard-boiled eggs

Greek yogurt

Dijon mustard

Celery

Green onions

Lettuce leaves

Method of Preparation:

1. Chop hard-boiled eggs, celery, and green onions.
2. In a bowl, mix eggs, Greek yogurt, Dijon mustard, celery, and green onions.
3. Spoon the egg salad onto lettuce leaves, creating wraps.

Salmon and Avocado Wrap

Preparation Time: 20 minutes

Serves: 4

Calories: 300

Ingredients:

Salmon fillets

Whole-grain wraps

Ripe avocados

Greek yogurt

Lemon juice

Fresh dill

Salt and pepper

Lettuce leaves (optional)

Method of Preparation:

1. Season salmon fillets with salt and pepper, then grill or bake until cooked.

2. In a bowl, mash avocados and mix with Greek yogurt, lemon juice, and chopped fresh dill.

3. Spread the avocado mixture onto whole-grain wraps.

4. Place a portion of cooked salmon on each wrap.

5. Optionally, add lettuce leaves for freshness.

6. Roll up the wraps and secure with toothpicks if needed.

Chicken and Rice Soup

Preparation Time: 40 minutes

Serves: 6

Calories: 200

Ingredients:

Chicken breast

Brown rice

Carrots

Celery

Onion

Garlic

Low-sodium chicken broth

Thyme

Bay leaves

Salt and pepper

Method of Preparation:

1. In a pot, sauté chopped onions and garlic until softened.
2. Add chicken breast, brown rice, carrots, celery, thyme, and bay leaves.
3. Pour in low-sodium chicken broth and bring to a simmer.
4. Cook until chicken is done and rice is tender.
5. Season with salt and pepper.

Ginger Carrot Soup

Preparation Time: 30 minutes

Serves: 4

Calories: 150

Ingredients:

Carrots

Onion

Ginger

Vegetable broth

Coconut milk

Olive oil

Salt and pepper

Method of Preparation:

1. Sauté chopped onions, grated ginger, and sliced carrots in olive oil until softened.
2. Pour in vegetable broth and simmer until carrots are tender.
3. Blend the mixture until smooth.
4. Stir in coconut milk and season with salt and pepper.
5. Simmer for a few more minutes.

DINNER

Salmon and Avocado Sushi Bowls

Preparation Time: 30 minutes

Serves: 4

Calories: 350

Ingredients:

Salmon fillets

Sushi rice

Avocados

Cucumber

Carrots

Soy sauce

Rice vinegar

Sesame seeds

Nori strips (optional)

Method of Preparation:

1. Cook sushi rice according to package instructions.
2. Season salmon with salt and pepper, then grill or bake until cooked.
3. Dice avocados, cucumber, and carrots.
4. In a bowl, assemble sushi bowls with rice, salmon, diced vegetables, and nori strips.
5. Drizzle with soy sauce and rice vinegar.
6. Sprinkle sesame seeds on top.

Roasted Vegetable Quiche

Preparation Time: 45 minutes

Serves: 6

Calories: 250

Ingredients:

Pie crust (store-bought or homemade)

Eggs

Milk (dairy or plant-based)

Mixed vegetables (e.g., bell peppers, zucchini, cherry tomatoes)

Cheese (optional)

Olive oil

Salt and pepper

Method of Preparation:

1. Preheat the oven to 375°F (190°C).
2. Roll out pie crust and fit it into a pie dish.
3. Whisk eggs and milk in a bowl, season with salt and pepper.
4. Sauté mixed vegetables in olive oil until slightly softened.
5. Place sautéed vegetables in the pie crust, pour egg mixture over them.
6. Add optional cheese on top.
7. Bake for 30-35 minutes or until the quiche is set.

Creamy Butternut Squash Soup

Preparation Time: 40 minutes

Serves: 4

Calories: 180

Ingredients:

Butternut squash

Onion

Garlic

Vegetable broth

Coconut milk

Olive oil

Nutmeg

Salt and pepper

Method of Preparation:

1. Peel and cube butternut squash, chop onions and garlic.
2. Sauté onions and garlic in olive oil until softened.
3. Add butternut squash, vegetable broth, and simmer until squash is tender.
4. Blend the mixture until smooth.
5. Stir in coconut milk, nutmeg, salt, and pepper.

6. Simmer for a few more minutes.

Chickpea and Spinach Curry

Preparation Time: 30 minutes

Serves: 4

Calories: 220

Ingredients:

Chickpeas (canned, drained)

Spinach

Onion

Tomatoes

Coconut milk

Garlic

Ginger

Curry spices (turmeric, cumin, coriander)

Olive oil

Salt and pepper

Method of Preparation:

1. Sauté chopped onions, garlic, and ginger in olive oil until softened.
2. Add curry spices and stir for a minute.
3. Add chopped tomatoes, chickpeas, and coconut milk.
4. Simmer until the sauce thickens.
5. Add spinach and cook until wilted.
6. Season with salt and pepper.

Baked Turkey Meatballs with Zucchini Noodles

Preparation Time: 40 minutes

Serves: 4

Calories: 300

Ingredients:

Ground turkey

Breadcrumbs (whole wheat for a healthier option)

Egg

Garlic powder

Italian seasoning

Zucchini

Tomato sauce (low sodium)

Olive oil

Salt and pepper

Method of Preparation:

1. Preheat the oven to 375°F (190°C).
2. In a bowl, combine ground turkey, breadcrumbs, egg, garlic powder, and Italian seasoning.
3. Form the mixture into meatballs and place them on a baking sheet.
4. Bake meatballs for 20-25 minutes.
5. Spiralize zucchini into noodles.
6. Sauté zucchini noodles in olive oil until tender.
7. Serve meatballs over zucchini noodles with tomato sauce.
8. Season with salt and pepper.

Mashed Sweet Potatoes with Grilled Chicken

Preparation Time: 40 minutes

Serves: 4

Calories: 350

Ingredients:

Sweet potatoes

Chicken breasts

Olive oil

Garlic powder

Paprika

Milk (dairy or plant-based)

Butter or margarine

Salt and pepper

Method of Preparation:

1. Peel and cube sweet potatoes.
2. Boil until tender, then drain.

3. Grill chicken breasts seasoned with olive oil, garlic powder, and paprika.

4. Mash sweet potatoes with milk, butter, salt, and pepper.

5. Serve grilled chicken over mashed sweet potatoes.

Baked Chicken with Sweet Potatoes and Green Beans

Preparation Time: 35 minutes

Serves: 4

Calories: 300

Ingredients:

Chicken thighs or breasts

Sweet potatoes

Green beans

Olive oil

Garlic powder

Rosemary

Salt and pepper

Method of Preparation:

1. Preheat the oven to 400°F (200°C).
2. Season chicken with olive oil, garlic powder, rosemary, salt, and pepper.
3. Peel and cube sweet potatoes, trim green beans.
4. Arrange chicken, sweet potatoes, and green beans on a baking sheet.
5. Bake for 25-30 minutes or until chicken is cooked through.

Ginger Turmeric Chicken Soup

Preparation Time: 45 minutes

Serves: 6

Calories: 250

Ingredients:

Chicken breasts

Chicken broth (low-sodium)

Ginger

Turmeric

Garlic

Carrots

Celery

Onion

Brown rice or quinoa

Salt and pepper

Method of Preparation:

1. In a pot, combine chicken broth, ginger, turmeric, minced garlic, carrots, celery, and onion.
2. Bring to a simmer and add chicken breasts.
3. Cook until chicken is done, then shred it.
4. Add brown rice or quinoa to the pot and cook until tender.
5. Season with salt and pepper to taste.

Cauliflower and Broccoli Gratin

Preparation Time: 40 minutes

Serves: 4

Calories: 200

Ingredients:

Cauliflower

Broccoli

Milk (dairy or plant-based)

Flour

Butter or margarine

Cheese (gruyere or cheddar)

Nutmeg

Bread crumbs (optional)

Salt and pepper

Method of Preparation:

1. Steam cauliflower and broccoli until tender.
2. In a saucepan, make a roux with flour and butter.
3. Gradually add milk to the roux, stirring continuously until it thickens.
4. Stir in grated cheese until melted.
5. Add nutmeg, salt, and pepper to taste.

6. Place steamed cauliflower and broccoli in a baking dish.

7. Pour the cheese sauce over the vegetables.

8. Optionally, sprinkle with bread crumbs.

9. Bake until golden and bubbly.

Lentil and Vegetable Stew

Preparation Time: 45 minutes

Serves: 6

Calories: 180

Ingredients:

Lentils

Vegetable broth (low-sodium)

Carrots

Celery

Onion

Tomatoes

Garlic

Cumin

Paprika

Bay leaves

Olive oil

Spinach

Lemon juice

Salt and pepper

Method of Preparation:

1. In a pot, sauté chopped onions and garlic in olive oil until softened.
2. Add lentils, vegetable broth, carrots, celery, diced tomatoes, cumin, paprika, and bay leaves.
3. Simmer until lentils and vegetables are tender.
4. Stir in spinach until wilted.
5. Season with lemon juice, salt, and pepper.

CONCLUSION

In conclusion, this cookbook is a kind travel companion, providing physical sustenance as well as a wellspring of hope and useful advice for a difficult journey.

Its dishes are thoughtfully designed to meet your particular dietary needs while receiving chemotherapy.

In addition to placing a high value on taste and variety, the book also stresses how crucial it is to include components that can help with side effect management and general wellbeing.

The cookbook offers a wide range of alternatives that accommodate shifting preferences and appetites, ensuring that you keep a positive relationship with food even in the face of treatment-related obstacles.

It encourages proactive self-care by giving you a sense of agency and control over their health.

Incorporating personal narratives and guidance from those who have experienced comparable journeys fosters a feeling of camaraderie and mutual comprehension, serving as a reminder to you that you are not alone in their experiences.

Made in the USA
Las Vegas, NV
18 December 2024